INSTRUCTOR'S MANUAL

ESSENTIALS of GEOLOGY

Brainerd Mears, Jr.
University of Wyoming

D. VAN NOSTRAND COMPANY
New York · Cincinnati · Toronto · London · Melbourne

D. Van Nostrand Company International offices:
London   Toronto   Melbourne

Manufactured in the United States of America.

Published by D. Van Nostrand Company
450 West 33rd. Street, New York, N.Y. 10001

10 9 8 7 6 5 4 3 2 1

PREFACE

This instructor's manual is designed to accompany <u>Essentials of Geology</u>. The manual deals with the overall organization of the textbook, and comments on science as it relates to geology. For each of the book's chapters, the manual contains a brief statement of the content, suggested treatment of the subject matter, and a group of multiple choice questions. The manual also contains a list of accessory materials and their sources that might be of interest.

Brainerd Mears, Jr.

Contents

ABOUT SCIENCE

<u>A</u> <u>Method</u>: Because it is a science, many people instinc-
tively believe geology is mysterious and difficult. It seems
to them a wonderland of fantastic theories, spectacular results, and absolute certainty somehow mixed with cautious
hedging and dull, tedious, detailed work. They believe it
is a form of magic whose practitioners talk in incomprehen-
sible jargon and sometimes write in mathematical symbols.
Science need not be that confusing, although any attempt to
explain it in bare outline is bound to be greatly oversimplified. Ignored are the challenging and interesting parts of
the story: the complications, pitfalls, and blind alleys
that reflect lack of evidence, misinterpreted observations,
conflicting points of view wrong conclusions, and human pre-
judice.

Whatever science is, and opinions differ, it somehow involves an art or method. To begin with, there are no cook-
book rules, or detailed instructions, that guarantee success
(else the discovery of a new natural law would be an elementary outside exercise). A physicist using a cyclotron or
atom smasher; a chemist working with a jungle of glass tubing;
a biologist studying a rat's tissue under a microscope; and
a geologist hammering on a rock ledge are all using different
detailed methods and techniques. Yet in a very general way,
all scientific work has a common pattern that in some ways
(but not all) resembles detective work. Both involve tackling
problems by collecting facts and observations and reaching
conclusions that are carefully tested and presented to a court
for judgment.

In any science, the careful detailed work is the collecting of evidence and the testing of theories. The fantastic
theories represent explanations and conclusions. The scientists are just detectives, of a sort, whose vocabulary and
symbols are open to anyone with sufficient interest and pa-
tience. The court of judgment consists of fellow scientists.

<u>Induction</u> <u>and</u> <u>Deduction</u>: In general, there are two broad
aspects to all methods used in natural science: creating new
ideas and testing them. It may be a matter of controlled
imagination. The creative part involves the inductive approach, wherein facts and observations are gathered and from
them a general explanation is made showing how the observations are related. You may use a very simple form of induc-
tion when faced wtih the problem that your car won't start.
You observe that the tank has gas, that the starter works,
that it is a very cold morning. From this you might propose
a possible explanation, that ice is blocking the fuel line.
Unlike this over-simple example, however, the significant observations in science are seldom easy to sort out and the
explanations are rarely obvious. How a scientist makes the
step from collecting observations to creating possible explana-

1

tions is difficult to say. It is not a matter of carefully
following the rules of logic. Reasoning by analogy may help,
but guesses, intuition, and sudden inspirations all play a
part. The one essential characteristic of a great scientist
seems to be a lively imagination.

In any case, once a possible explanation is proposed it
must be carefully tested. Here logical rules do help. Deduc-
tive logic assumes that if the explanation is correct, certain
consequences, which can be checked, should follow. In the
case of the stalled car, if the fuel lines are iced, then warming them should permit the car to start. If this test fails,
then some other explanation is in order. When a scientist
feels he has an acceptable explanation, he brings it to trial
by publishing it in a scientific journal. Then other interested workers critically examine the idea and do further check-
ing which will determine whether the idea is accepted, reworked
and modified, or rejected.

What we have called "explanations" vary in reliability. If
speculative ideas need much more testing, or verification,
they are classed as hypotheses. Hypotheses, even if eventually
disproved, serve a very useful function, for they eliminate
aimless groping by giving direction to further investigations
designed to substantiate or disprove them. Well-tested hypotheses supported by strong evidence become accepted as theories.
They represent the consensus of opinion at a given time.

Mental Images: Unlike some philosophers, scientists assume
there is a real world of nature, and they believe-on faith
alone-that nature is orderly and its relationships discover-
able. But our knowledge of the world outside us comes only
through our "pipelines" of sense perception: sight, hearing,
touch, taste, and smell. Instruments from great telescopes
searching the macrocosm of outer space to electron microscopes
probing the microcosm of molecular and crystal structure have
incredibly expanded man's unaided powers of observation. None-
theless, we cannot claim that our descriptions are the real
world; they are only human ideas about nature in our present
state of understanding.

Thus, scientific hypotheses and theories are now often considered models--important ideas. The concept of the hydrogen
atom as a central nucleus with an orbital electron was called
a model by Niels Bohr in 1913, and since then other schemes
have been considered models. A road map is a model. It may
be very sketchy, leaving out most features of the area represented, but if it allows prediction of the best route for a
trip, it is a useful model. Miniature streams are created
for geologic laboratory studies to help in visualizing the
operation of rivers. But a trickle of water through sand in
a tank is not a river. It is a model, a much simpler system
lacking many features of the real thing. Scientific models

may be physical models like atom diagrams, verbal models
describing in   words what cannot be pictured (like energy),
or mathematical models giving the equations for concepts.
Most diagrams in science textbooks are models.

Since hypothetical and theoretical schemes are based on
limited observations, models may fail in the test of successful prediction. Scientific knowledge is not divine revela-
tion but rather human interpretation subject to error and
change. Even so, it is the most exact and carefully tested
general knowledge available to man.

Accumulated Knowledge: Science has been likened to a sky-
scraper in which the top floor is still being built while the
other floors are occupied. The part in use represents a vast
inventory of accumulated knowledge, a consistent body of
accepted fact and well-established theory. The level under
construction represents the forefront of science--the areas
of current research where speculative ideas and models are
being proposed and tested. Many will be rejected, most others
will probably be changed before being integrated into the
general structure. Although the many rejected ideas are now
history and part of modern science, their past existence re-
veals much about the nature of science.

Geology, like any science, has a large base of well-tested,
reliable knowledge not likely to be overturned, and an outer
realm of current problems when concepts are sifted by scientific method. A geologist must be versed in many of the established schemes common to all science: the models of atomic
structure used by chemists, for example. His or her way of
thinking is also instinctively influenced by broad, reliable
geologic concepts. While many people assume unchanging rocks
and eternal hills, the geologist envisions an ever-changing
Earth of decaying rocks and ephemeral mountains, a concept
interwoven with another--the enormity of geologic time. Geologists evaluate and tackle current problems of research in light
of their extensive, ingrained backgrounds in well-established
ideas (the paradigm). No short course can make you a geologist,
but it can provide a great appreciation of the Earth around
you, and help answer the question, what is geology?

THE PLAN OF THE BOOK

The textbook accompanying this manual gives a general survey of physical geology. It briefly touches on the nature of present-day geology and reviews the history of the people and ideas that laid the groundwork for modern science. Introducing geology with a bit of history is not a new approach (it was used by Charles Lyell in his _Principles of Geology_ over a century ago), but it gives, I think, a proper introduction to the nature of geology as a science. Then, an overall view of the Earth as a planet is given and the chapter ends with the developments leading to the plate tectonic scheme for the Earth's internal dynamics. The next section takes a closer look at the materials of the Earth--its minerals and rocks, and how they provide the bases for the principles and techniques of reconstructing Earth history. The following section discusses how the Earth's materials are assembled into the major crustal structures and the dynamics involved, earthquakes and the planet's internal architecture, igneous activity associated with volcanic and plutonic forms, and the crustal deformation involved in mountain building, continents and ocean basins. After the constructional features of the lithosphere have been dealt with, weathering, mass gravity movements, and the major erosional agents that tend to grade, or wear down, the face of the Earth are introduced.

This is followed by a discussion of the changing theories of the origin and history of some of the Earth's major mountain ranges in light of older and more recent concepts of the lithosphere's mechanics. This structure naturally leads to consideration of intriguing geologic problems of the future. The text concludes by discussing how the study of geology and Earth history provide the basis for intelligent planning to meet some of mankind's most critical present and future problems involving the Earth's environment and energy resources.

Not all teachers will agree with this order of presentation. Some may prefer to follow a treatment of the Earth's materials with a discussion of gradational processes before considering geologic structures--an equally valid order for the presentation of physical geology. Whatever order is preferred, the presentation in the text is flexible enough to allow various chapters to be skipped or presented out of sequence.

Chapter One

THE SCIENCE OF THE EARTH

To introduce geology, the text considers its present-day content and scope and reviews the historical development of some of its fundamental concepts. Some students may believe - mistakenly - that memorizing the latest facts and theories is all that's needed to understand a science. To ignore former concepts and theories as useless knowledge, "boring old stuff," is to miss the mainstream of a science A knowledge of the latest findings is important, but in ten years much of the information may be out of date. One must have a sense of the historical development of its schemes to know what geology, or any science, involves. Moreover, by studying past human endeavors to understand the Earth, perhaps we can avoid making the same old mistakes. And in the end, the history of geology should provide a fascinating story for potential scientists and nonscientists alike.

Multiple Choice Questions

1. Geology is:

   a. primarily concerned with man's interaction with the environment.
   b. a less basic science than mathematics, but more so than physics and chemistry.
   c. such a "Mickey Mouse" subject that any college freshman can pass it without studying or going to class.
   d. like astronomy in seeking to understand a place, rather than produce universal principles for matter and energy in general.
   e. based on theories, hypotheses, and working hypotheses that give absolutely certain explanations for Earth features and mechanisms.

2. The doctrine of uniformitarianism:

   a. holds that all geologic changes are very slow and never violent.
   b. was accepted by most competent geologists soon after it was proposed by Dr. Hutton.
   c. requires an appreciation of the great length of geologic time.
   d. was the basis for Georges Cuvier's theory of the origins of the Earth's physical features and the forms of past life.
   e. resulted from discoveries made possible by the instrumental revolution.

3. Professor Adam G. Werner of the School of Mines at Freiberg, Saxony (in Germany):

$\underline{a}$. was an inspiring teacher who believed that geologic
   features result from natural processes and who made
   major contributions to the study of minerals.
b. held that volcanos are created suddenly in single, catastrophic eruptions.
c. proclaimed that the ultimate purpose of geology is to
   demonstrate the truth of Biblical Scripture.
d. was a leader in the discovery that basalt and granite
   are igneous rocks that solidified from molten materials.
e. proposed a theory that eventually was proven by Charles
   Lyell.

4. Concerning the concept of organic evolution:

   a. it became generally accepted by scientists after the
      literate Scotch editor, Robert Chambers, clearly explain-
      ed the ideas of Charles Darwin in the book, <u>Vestiges of
      Creation</u>.
   b. although of great interest to scientists in the nine-
      teenth century, was of little interest and largely un-
      known to the educated public.
   c. evolution is today generally thought to result from the
      use and disuse of animal organs, the theory presented
      by Jean Baptiste Lamarck.
   d. the great geologists, Adam Sedgwick, George Cuvier, and
      William Buckland, although originally skeptical of the
      theory, came to accept it when the evidence became con-
      vincing.
   $\underline{e}$. it was presented in an epic poem by Charles Darwin's
      grandfather, Erasmus.

5. Nineteenth century geology demonstrates that:

   a. the controversies then were basically a battle between
      science and religion.
   b. scientists invariably use an open-minded and unbiased
      approach in evaluating other scientists' concepts and
      theories.
   $\underline{c}$. the general climate of political and social opinion can
      influence scientists in their acceptance or rejection
      of a new theory.
   d. given adequate money, science can solve any problem.
   e. that the concepts and theories of scientists are totally
      incomprehensible to intelligent nonscientists.

Chapter Two

THE PLANET EARTH

To begin discussion of the Earth, we present a global model that provides an overall view of the planet's features as they would be seen by an astronaut in space. Most of these external aspects are certainly well-known to most students, but the subtle reasoning that led to the discovery of these features--seemingly self-evident in the space age--is not often common knowledge. The determinations of the Earth's shape and size in classical Greek times were major scientific discoveries, and the later determinations of the Earth's motions were the major breakthrough that, quite literally, marks the beginning of the Scientific Revolution in human thinking. The logic used in these determinations is the same sort that scientists use today. This gives the presentation of examples from history considerable educational merit. An added advantage of historical examples is that they are comprehensible to most students at the freshman college level. Such case histories do not require the training in mathematical and physical manipulations that obscure the exciting research findings in modern geophysical studies of the Earth's interior from the intelligent layman, even though the basic logic and reasoning have changed little through the ages.

The preliminary introduction of the plate tectonic scheme completes the Earth model with modern concepts of the Earth's interior. It also gives the student a frame of reference--the one now used by most professional geologists--that provides an integrating theme for the material discussed in later chapters. The discussion of the emergence of the plate tectonic concept completes the history of geology begun in chapter one and, perhaps most importantly, is a basis for reflections on the human side of scientific investigations. Certainly, the interaction of normal and revolutionary science is ideally illustrated by the rise of "the new world view"--the plate tectonic scheme.

Multiple Choice Questions

1. That the Earth is generally spherical is <u>not</u> proven by:

   a. gravity measurements at different places on the Earth's surface.
   <u>b</u>. the voyage of Magellan's crew around the Earth.
   c̲. the constant rate of disappearance of ships at sea.
   d. the Earth's shadow in a lunar eclipse.
   e. the North Star's elevation above the horizon at different latitudes.

2. The Earth's revolution in orbit:

   <u>a</u>. is demonstrated by parallax of stars.

b. causes long range cannon shells shot either south or
   north in the northern hemisphere to be deflected to
   the right.
c. affects the shape of the Earth.
d. causes the path of a pendulum to shift clockwise in
   the northern hemisphere.
e. gives a point on the equator a velocity of almost 25,000
   miles per hour.

3. When Eratosthenes calculated the Earth's circumference, he:

   a. was the first to demonstrate the Earth's oblateness.
   b. would have obtained the distance around the Earth, even
      if the Earth were not generally spherical.
   c. knew the distance to the Earth's center before he made
      his calculations.
   d. assumed that the Sun's rays were parallel (at the same
      time) at Syene and Alexandria.
   e. used the wrong method, but luckily got the right answer
      through compensating errors.

4. The Earth has a:

   a. rock surface as smooth as a billiard ball in proportion
      to its size.
   b. diameter of about 4000 miles.
   c. land area of about 71%.
   d. density of about 2.7 for the whole Earth.
   e. local relief of about 12 miles.

5. The Earth's mass was determined by:

   a. Sir Isaac Newton.
   b. using a pycnometer to obtain the specific gravity of
      average crustal rock.
   c. first obtaining the universal gravitational constant.
   d. measuring the shift in direction of a swinging Foucault
      pendulum.
   e. using the equation $E = MC^2$.

6. The total relief of the Earth is:

   a. close to 1% of the Earth's diameter.
   b. less than half the Earth's oblateness.
   c. the vertical difference between valley bottoms and the
      mountain peaks in a particular region.
   d. borne largely by United States Foreign Aid programs
   e. the vertical difference between sea level and the great-
      est elevation of the lithosphere.

7. A revolution in studies of the topography of the deep ocean
   resulted from:

   a. the invention of underwater cameras.
   b. the use of echo sounding devices.

c. the British Challenger expedition.
d. scuba diving techniques
e. the development of submarines.

8. Mid-oceanic ridge systems:

a. are composed largely of granitic rocks.
b. have graben-like valleys along the length of their crests.
c. are stable belts with few earthquakes and little volcanic
    activity.
d. are entirely submarine features that nowhere rise above
    sea level.
e. probably consist of deposits eroded from the continental
    masses.

9. The plate tectonic mechanism:

a. was proposed a hundred years ago, although not generally
    accepted until the 1920s.
b. is supported by several separate lines of geophysical
    and geological evidence.
c. most certainly is caused by convection currents in the
    Earth's mantle.
d. has been rejected by most American geologists but support-
    ed by geologists in the southern hemisphere.
e. cannot be related to the deep oceanic trenches.

10. Which of the following is not somehow related to the pre-
    sent-day paradigm (the currently accepted pattern of inter-
    related facts and schemes) of geology?

a. the probability of future modifications and changes in
    geologic explanations.
b. the theory that after its early molten stage, the Earth
    has gradually cooled off and contracted until it is now
    in an Ice Age.
c. the concepts of an ever-changing Earth and of its life-
    forms during an enormous span of time.
d. a recent revolution in geologic thinking.
e. lectures, textbook readings, and laboratory exercises.

Chapter Three

MATTER AND MINERALS

A very elementary discussion of chemistry precedes our introduction to minerals. Since the chemistry background of students may vary considerably, the opening sections can be skimmed by some readers and carefully studied by others. Instructors can start directly with minerals, if they so choose.

In a general survey of geology, students may become discouraged if overloaded with a large number of minerals whose chemical formulae, physical properties, and uses must be memorized. The discussion in the text therefore, is limited to a few essential rock-forming minerals that will be encountered later on and a few of special interest. For more interested students, there are many good books on rocks and minerals.

Laboratory experience that emphasizes careful examination of minerals is most desirable, but if the course has no laboratory, boxes of minerals can be distributed for study during discussions or lectures, or colored slides of minerals can be shown. Although memorization of any but the simplest mineral formulae will probably not be long retained, the student should gain a generalized knowledge of the elements present in minerals as background for later study of the rocks of the Earth's crust. In general, internal structure and its relations to mineral properties should be emphasized where possible.

<u>Multiple Choice Questions</u>

1. A chemical compound:

    a. contains only one kind of atom throughout.
    <u>b</u>. always contains the same proportions of elements.
    c. is a solid by definition.
    d. usually closely resembles the elements it is composed of.
    e. is a mixture.

2. Atoms:

    a. are the ultimate, indivisible solid particles of which all matter is composed.
    b. were first proposed as a concept by John Dalton.
    <u>c</u>. become electrically charged upon gaining or losing an outer electron.
    d. always have the same number of orbital electrons as neutrons in the nucleus.
    e. can be split by ordinary chemical reactions.

3. Isotopes:

   a. have the same chemical properties in a given element.
   b. have identical weights in the same element.
   c. are lines of equal topographic elevation.
   d. result from ionic bonding of elements.
   e. occur in uranium but not hydrogen.

4. Which is _not_ correct?

   a. all natural compounds are minerals.
   b. all minerals are crystalline.
   c. some minerals consist of a single element.
   d. rocks are composed of minerals.
   e. quantitative analyses of most minerals require elaborate
      laboratory equipment and trained personnel.

5. The internal crystalline structure of minerals:

   a. is characteristic of all solids.
   b. causes all crystals of a given mineral to have the same
      outer shape and size.
   c. was verified by the use of X-rays.
   d. was first carefully worked out for the mineral quartz.
   e. can be observed with powerful optical microscopes.

6. Which is correct?

   a. all minerals with good crystal faces have good cleavage.
   b. two minerals of the same chemical composition always
      have the same hardness.
   c. specific gravity of minerals is usually stated in terms
      of Moh's scale.
   d. mineral luster results from minute impurities.
   e. a single mineral type may occur in different colors.

7. The most abundant element in the Earth's crust is:

   a. silicon.
   b. aluminum.
   c. oxygen.
   d. water.
   e. iron.

8. Which mineral contains _none_ of the four most abundant elements in the Earth's crust?

   a. calcite.
   b. feldspar.
   c. olivine.
   d. halite.
   e. quartz.

9. The silica tetrahedron:

    a. is the basic building block of the Earth's hydrosphere.
    b. was discovered by measuring the angles between faces
       of crystals.
    c. is the principal constituent of calcite.
    d. is found only in minerals with good cleavage.
    e. has four ions of oxygen.

10. Which is not correct?

    a. quartz contains only the two most abundant minerals in
       the Earth's crust.
    b. feldspar is the most abundant mineral in the Earth's
       crust.
    c. mica has only one good cleavage direction.
    d. ferromagnesian minerals are usually dark colored.
    e. clay commonly results from the weathering of quartz.

Chapter Four

ROCKS, THE MAJOR GROUPS

The three major rock groups are discussed. For each,
essential description and classification are given along
with a discussion of the geologic significance and orgin
of the rocks.

A true appreciation of rocks, as of minerals, comes only
from handling specimens, but slides are again helpful when
a laboratory is not available. If equipment is available
for projecting thin sections, this will certainly increase
interest, and the optics involved need not be gone into at
great depth. Rocks, as well as many other aspects of geology,
can best be taught by observing relations in the field, although this may be impossible for various practical reasons.

As in chapter two, it is probably best to bear down on a
number of varieties of a few important rock types that will
be mentioned in later chapters rather than introducing an
overabundance that will probably be indigestible to many students. Since rocks are the basis of much that follows, this
chapter should receive careful attention. Besides inculcat-
ing a "feeling" for rock types, the chapter gives the opportunity for a review of minerals and introduces the use of
rocks in interpretation of Earth history based on the princi-
ple of Uniformitarianism.

Multiple Choice Questions

1. Which would most likely produce a glassy igneous rock?

    a. a ferromagnesian intrusion.
    b. slow metamorphism of shale.
    c. rapid chilling of lava.
    d. slow cooling of viscous magma.
    e. crystal growth by slow cooling of a highly viscous magma.

2. Porphyries:

    a. are purple-colored rocks.
    b. characterize batholiths.
    c. lack minerals with crystalline structure.
    d. result when initially intrusive magma is later erupted.
    e. are the extrusive equivalent of amphibolites.

3. Which mineral characterizes granite?

    a. plagioclase feldspar.
    b. calcite
    c. K-feldspar.
    d. augite.
    e. olivine.

4. The rock having the same minerals as gabbro is:

    a. andesite.
    b. diorite.
    c. rhyolite.
    d. peridotite.
    e. basalt.

5. Sedimentary facies are:

    a. evidences of past life.
    b. the eroded topographic surfaces of exposed sedimentary layers.
    c. lateral changes in rock materials that were deposited at the same
       time.
    d. extensive strata whose rocks are all of a single sedimentary type.
    e. the basic units in geologic mapping.

6. The best indication that sedimentary rocks originated in shallow water
   is:

    a. clastic texture.
    b. ripple marks.
    c. mud cracks.
    d. concretions.
    e. cross-bedding.

7. The geologic conditions indicated by an arkose are:

    a. hydration.
    b. long weathering of rocks containing K-feldspars.
    c. active uplift and rapid deposition in deeply subsiding troughs nearby.
    d. mechanical weathering and erosion of granite in a nearby region of
       high relief.
    e. much churning and stirring of beach sands by waves for a long time
       before being lithified.

8. Metamorphic rocks:

    a. all form thousands of feet below the Earth's surface.
    b. may result from volcanic activity.
    c. always have flat mineral crystals such as mica.
    d. always contain minerals that existed in their parent rock before
       metamorphism.
    e. were once magma.

9. Which metamorphic rock would not have foliation?

    a. gneiss.
    b. garnet
    c. phyllite.
    d. schist.
    e. hornfels.

10. According to plate tectonic theory:

   a. ophiolite suites are the hotel rooms where geologists meet to
      discuss plate tectonic theory.
   b. melanges result from the crushing of the well-washed sands, shales,
      and limestones deposited in miogeosynclines.
   c. magmatic belts of plutoic crystalline, igneous and metamorphic
      rocks are created in mid-oceanic ridges where global plates are
      splitting and drifting apart.
   d. the rise of mountains along colliding continental and oceanic
      plates create clastic wedges of erosional debris that is shed
      towards continental interiors.
   e. all worthwhile problems involving the origin, classification, and
      distribution of rocks have been solved.

<u>Matching</u> (insert letter by proper answer in list two in blank in front of
question in list one).

List No. 1	List No. 2

<u>List No. 1</u>

1.___A mineral containing no silicon.   (I)

2.___A mineral composed entirely of the
     two most abundant chemical elements
     in the Earth's crust.   (K)

3.___A non-crystalline silicate.   (D)

4.___Number 7 on Moho's scale of
     hardness.   (K)

5.___An aphanitic igneous rock.   (A)

6.___A coarse-grained igneous rock con-
     taining no quartz.   (L)

7.___Some geologists think it is mainly
     an igneous rock, but others think
     it is mainly metamorphic.   (N)

8.___An organic sedimentary rock.   (G)

9.___A clastic sedimentary rock.   (E)

10.___A metamorphic rock produced solely
     by contact metamorphism of fine-
     grained clastic rocks.   (J)

<u>List No. 2</u>

A. basalt
B. porphyry
C. asbestos
D. obsidian
E. claystone
F. slate
G. coal
H. hornblende
I. calcite
J. hornfels
K. quartz
L. gabbro
M. feldspar
N. granite

15

Chapter Five

ROCKS AND FOSSILS AS RECORDS OF GEOLOGIC TIME

Since geology is fundamentally _the_ historical physical-and-biological science, its hard-won methods of establishing time relationships are the essential tools without which a coherent Earth history could not be constructed. The development of techniques of relative dating and correlation were the necessary first steps in the eventual construction of the geologic time scale, one of the major scientific achievements of the nineteenth century. Interestingly, most of the pioneers who created the time scale (except for Charles Lyell) were catastrophist geologists who did not accept the concept of organic evolution. William Smith was unaware of the concept. Cuvier, Sedgewick, and Murchison strongly opposed the idea. Yet today, geologists recognize that it is the evolution of fossils that makes them the most important tools in relative dating. Thus the mere fact that fossils change and are different in vertical successions of layered rocks makes them indicators of the order of deposition, whatever the interpretations of why they differ.

Techniques of absolute time determinations (finite dating) are one of the most significant geologic developments stemming from the instrumental revolution and the use of the allied sciences in the twentieth century. These laboratory procedures provide check points in years on the geologic time scale and the dating and approximate correlation of the unfossiliferous igneous and metamorphic rocks, most notably those recording the Earth's long Precambrian history.

Some students may find parts of the chapter hard going, and some instructors may want to postpone it until later in the course. I have placed it here because it introduces the techniques that were essential for making geology and organized and coordinated science.

<u>Multiple Choice Questions</u>

1. Relative dating:

    a. gives the age in years of geologic events.
    b. can not be used if rocks are folded or faulted.
    c. applies only to sedimentary rocks.
    d. is no longer used by geologists.
    <u>e</u>. gives only the order in which geologic events occurred.

2. Concerning fossils, which is <u>not</u> true?

    a. they may occur in metamorphic rocks.
    b. their value for dating rocks was independently discovered by workers in France and in England at about the same time.
    c. they include actual animal remains, mineral replacements of animals, and even footprints.

d. in some cases identical groups characterize rocks of greatly
   different ages.
e. some show that certain animals have changed very little over
   long spans of geologic time.

3. Which is correct?

   a. calculations based on the salt in the oceans give a fairly
      accurate measure of the age of the Earth.

   b. Lord Kelvin's estimate of the age of the Earth was based on the
      book of Genesis.
   c. the rate of deposition applied to thick sections of sedimentary
      rocks is a generally reliable method for determining great inter-
      vals of finite time.
   d. varves have been reliably used for finite time determinations.
   e. most geologists immediately accepted Kelvin's figure for the age
      of the Earth.

4. Radioactive isotopes:

   a. are completely dead in twice the length of their half life.
   b. represent atoms that all disintegrate at the same time in a
      given mineral.
   c. all break down to form lead.
   d. decay to form different elements.
   e. are most useful in giving the date of such rocks as conglomerates.

5. Radiometric methods of dating:

   a. were used to construct the geologic time scale.
   b. can be used on some organic materials.
   c. can only give the age of the Earth.
   d. now indicate that the Earth's age is about two billion years.
   e. have been little improved in the last 25 years.

6. Correlation of rocks:

   a. determines that rocks are of the same origin.
   b. has been possible for most of the Earth's history by using fossils.
   c. is most safely done for widely separated outcrops by using litholo-
      gic similarity.
   d. is possible from one continent to another by means of fossils.
   e. is best done by using the colors of rocks.

7. The beach sandstones of a transgressive sea moving several hundred
   miles from east to west:

   a. could be represented in a particular place by basal limestone,
      middle shale, and upper sandstone.
   b. would be younger to the west than to the east.
   c. would probably be the same age throughout.
   d. would be part of a clastic debris flood.
   e. would indicate active mountain building in the western part of
      a geosyncline.

8. Geologic formations are:

   a. developed across continents with little change in character.
   b. named from rock type, color, or other distinct features.
   c. such things as geodes, ripple marks, volcanic bombs, and fossils.
   d. primarily easily described units that are convenient for mapping.
   e. single strata, showing no lateral variation.

9. The Geologic Time Scale:

   a. was constructed from a locality in England where a complete
      sequence of rocks of all ages was exposed in a single cliff.
   b. contains subdivisions called time-rock units.
   c. has major divisions called eras that are named after places.
   d. has divisions called periods that each represent 50 million
      years of Earth history.
   e. was worked out by geologists in the nineteenth century

THE VIBRANT EARTH AND ITS INTERIOR

The next three chapters deal with our knowledge of the Earth's deep interior and the constructional forces and features building and deforming the Earth's crust. Chapter six considers the directly observable phenomena of earthquakes, then their instrumental study, and lastly the internal zones of core, mantle, and crust.

The spectacular nature of earthquakes gives them a particular interest that can be exploited by accounts of the more spectacular. Moreover, earthquakes represent geologic forces in readily observable action that contrasts with the more subtle--but no less important--workings of the external geologic agents, previously considered. The dramatic approach to seismology is justified, but it should not obscure study of the evidence for the Earth's internal zones. That this evidence for an Earth model is based not on direct observation, but rather on interpretations of instrumental readings, is an evident but important point. A good understanding of theories about the architecture of the Earth's interior is essential for later discussions of speculations on the origins of volcanism and mountain building.

<u>Multiple Choice Questions</u>:

1. During a strong earthquake:

    a. solid bedrock, like granite, may be thrown into waves a foot or more high.
    b. strong winds are generated by the shaking
    c. a definite rumbling noise can be heard.
    <u>d</u>. the active fault may briefly open to become a gaping crack extending to great depths.
    e. destruction of buildings would be least near the epicenter.

2. The best rock on which a building would be constructed in an earthquake area is:

    a. shale.
    <u>b</u>. granite.
    c. moraine.
    d. flood plain deposits.
    e. swamp deposits.

3. If an earthquake strikes while you are eating in an old stone restaurant in a city, the best thing to do is:

    a. keep eating.
    <u>b</u>. dive under a stout table.
    c. get into the street fast.
    d. walk, don't run, to the nearest exit.
    e. send a postcard to a nearby seismograph station.

4. Displacement on a fault during a single earthquake would be closest
   to:

   a. 15 feet.
   b. 150 feet.
   c. 521 feet.
   d. several thousand feet.
   e. several miles.

5. Actual duration of a single shock in a strong earthquake would be
   closest to:

   a. two seconds.
   b. one minute.
   c. three minutes.
   d. fifteen minutes.
   e. several days.

6. Seismic intensity is:

   a. determined from instrumental observations.
   b. most pronounced in regions of crystalline rocks.
   c. based on observations any intelligent layman can make.
   d. the measure of earthquake strength at the focus.
   e. is directly proportional to distance from the epicenter.

7. Seismographs:

   a. operate best with a fixed base set in alluvium.
   b. only record earthquake foci less than 7000 miles away.
   c. have not detected earthquake foci in the Earth's mantle.
   d. depend on dynamic inertial reciprocity of lithofors.
   e. are basically a kind of pendulum.

8. Earthquake waves transmitted through the Earth's core are:

   a. "P" waves.
   b. permanent waves.
   c. "S" waves.
   d. all body waves.
   e. "L" waves.

9. The discovery of the boundary between the mantle and crust by
   Mohorovicic involved:

   a. the observation that up to a certain distance from an epicenter
      "S" waves arrive before "P" waves.
   b. the conclusion that beyond a certain distance from the eipcenter,
      deeper penetrating seismic waves arrive ahead of waves travelling
      a shorter distance and closer to the surface.
   c. the inference that the seismic "shadow zone" is caused by a major
      boundary within the Earth.
   d. the fact that "S" waves are damped out in liquids but "P" waves,
      although bent, are transmitted through liquids.
   e. deep drilling through the Earth's crust.

10. The Sial is:

    a. largely basaltic.
    b. absent from deep ocean basins.
    c. the upper part of the mantle.
    d. thin in folded mountains.
    e. sedimentary.

VOLCANISM

In chapter seven we discuss volcanic and related igneous activity that is responsible for often observable structures in the Earth's crust. Famous volcanic eruptions, the structure of volcanos and lava plateaus, and the structure of intrusive features are presented along with ideas on the nature of volcanic eruptions and the deeper sources of magma.

The material in this chapter gives the student an opportunity to review the previously discussed topic of igneous rocks. The dramatic nature of volcanic eruptions, as with earthquakes, can be used to stir student interest. It is probably worth pointing out that the internal structures of volcanoes and such features as stocks and laccoliths can be pieced together into reasonable models from the observation of deeply eroded forms. However, ideas on the nature of eruptions, models of deep source regions, and the sources of magma should be considered tentative because the processes involved operate in the unobservable base of the crust or in the mantle.

Multiple Choice Questions:

1. Volcanic ejecta:

   a. are all liquid and solid materials.
   b. may include steam released from magma.
   c. are called bombs if they explode on striking the ground.
   d. commonly consist of the ash and cinders from burning coal beds.
   e. sometimes include material from the Earth's core.

2. Which rock would most likely form most of a volcanic cone?

   a. quartz.
   b. gabbro.
   c. granite.
   d. ryolite
   e. eclogite.

3. Which is not correct?

   a. cinder cones consist entirely of volcanic bombs, cinders, and ash.
   b. strato-volcanos represent the largest masses of volcanic rock erupted on the Earth's crust.
   c. shield volcanos are mainly composed of lava.
   d. compound volcanos are produced by a major change in the type of eruption in a given volcano.
   e. a single lava plateau may extend over many thousands of square miles.

4. Which is correct?

   a. eruptions of the volcano Stromboli have been exceedingly violent.

b. the spine of Pelee was a typical example of a volcanic neck.
c. the catastrophic eruption of Krakatoa probably resulted from ocean water seeping down to hot magma.
d. Vesuvius has been continously active since before Roman times.
e. eruptions of the Hawaiian volcanos often involve lava flowing from cracks in the flanks of the volcanos.

5. Volcanos in general:

a. are the main subject of a branch of geology called seismology.
b. are now completely predictable in their times of eruption.
c. tend to coincide with the belts of active earthquakes and mountain building.
d. occur only in land areas.
e. are good evidence that the Earth's surface rocks are a relatively thin crust over a completely molten interior.

6. Sills are:

a. always horizontal.
b. younger than the rocks around them.
c. cut across preexisting structures.
d. of metamorphic origin.
e. extrusive igneous features that bake the rock under them.

7. The least violently explosive volcanos are:

a. cinder cones.
b. composed of basalt.
c. characterized by eruptions like Vesuvius.
d. largely composed of granite.
e. strato-volcanos.

8. The source of the magma creating volcanos is:

a. not definitely known.
b. in laccolith-shaped pockets inside volcanic cones.
c. burning pools of deep-seated oil.
d. from radioactive hot spots at the base of the Earth's crust.
e. from heat generated by slippage along deep-seated faults.

9. Bowen's reaction series:

a. absolutely requires that for an original basaltic magma to change to a final granitic composition the first-formed crystals must be removed from reaction with the remaining liquids.
b. is a theory that was based on careful field observations of rocks in batholiths.
c. explains how partial melting of a granitic tectonic plate could produce a basaltic magma.
d. states that quartz, then K-feldspar, then muscovite are the first crystals to form in a gradually cooling magma.
e. explains how the melting of sedimentary rocks in a geosyncline would produce a granitic magma.

10. Which is <u>not</u> true about batholiths?

    a. most geologists agree that they form in the "roots" of mountains.
    b. they are very large plutonic structures.
    <u>c</u>. they most likely represent intrusion of rock materials from the
       mantle into the crust.
    d. they consist mainly of granitic rocks.
    e. their boundaries with adjacent country rock may be either sharp or
       gradational.

<u>Matching</u> (insert letter by proper answer in list two in blank in front
of question in list one).

List No. 1	List No. 2

1. ___ Italian volcano having almost continuous eruptions throughout recorded history.

2. ___ In terms of total volume of material, probably the world's largest volcano erupted onto the Earth's crust.

3. ___ Eruption described by Pliny, the Younger, in letters to the historian, Tacitus.

4. ___ A compound volcano with a large cinder cone on its top.

5. ___ This eruption was heard 2000 miles away and caused great sea waves that went around the world.

6. ___ Archeological excavations indicate that a great eruption of this volcano had a catastrophic effect on the Minoan civilization.

List No. 2

A. Surtsey
B. Pelee
C. Santorini
D. Katmai
E. Tombolo
F. Mt. Hood
G. Pepperoni
H. Vesuvius
I. Mazama
J. Paricutin
K. Stromboli
L. Etna
M. Agung
N. Hawaii
O. Shasta
P. Roncalio
Q. Krakatoa
R. Ararat

Chapter Eight

THE DEFORMED CRUST

This chapter concludes the treatment of Earth structures as well as the major section on physical geology. It presents a discussion of crustal movements in historic times, describes folds and faults, broad types of deformation and regional structures, and concludes with various hypothetical mechanisms for the causes of mountain building.

One of the more important abilities required in structural geology is the ability to visualize relations in three dimensions. Outside exercises in the interpretation of simple diagrams of structural blocks and the drawing of geologic cross-sections from geologic maps are helpful in developing this ability. Some students will find such exercises easy; many can improve their ability to think in three dimensions; a few unfortunately will continue to have difficulty. The discussion of the causes of mountain building again illustrates the problem of constructing successful models for the operation of the Earth's deep internal processes, but it should be emphasized that the various contending hypotheses are useful because they give direction to geologic research by motivating a search for better evidence.

<u>Multiple Choice Questions</u>:

1. A fold whose axial plane is horizontal must be:

   a. overturned.
   <u>b</u>. recumbent.
   c. plunging.
   d. isoclinal.
   e. upright.

2. The youngest beds on a geologic map would be in the center of a(n):

   a. eroded anticline.
   b. hogback.
   c. valley in horizontal strata.
   <u>d</u>. eroded syncline.

3. A fault whose footwall side has moved up relative to its hanging wall side is:

   a. strike-slip.
   <u>b</u>. normal.
   c. thrust.
   d. abnormal.
   e. reverse.

4. If active movement on a fault with some strike-slip movement creates
   a scarp, the fault is:

   a. normal.
   b. reverse.
   c. thrust.
   d. strike-slip
   e. oblique-slip.

5. An angular unconformity:

   a. has older rocks on top of younger.
   b. results from: (1) deposition, (2) erosion, (3) renewed deposition
      (4) deformation, in that order.
   c. is harder to recognize in the field than a disconformity.
   d. always contains a buried erosion surface.
   e. has beds with the same dip and strike at top and bottom.

6. Epeirogenic uplift:

   a. can raise rocks thousands of feet without sharp folding.
   b. is building up of the crust by volcanic eruption.
   c. results from the drift of continental blocks over the underlying
      basalt.
   d. is responsible for intensely folded structures as are found
      in the Alps.
   e. has caused the San Andreas rift.

7. The concept of isostacy:

   a. involves the idea of continents "floating" on denser plastic rocks.
   b. has been rejected on evidence from seismology.
   c. was proposed after Radhakrishhan found his accurate pendulum
      chronometer gaining time when used in the Himalaya mountains.
   d. requires that mountains are held up by the strength of the Earth's
      crust.
   e. In Archdeacon Pratt's model, assumes the Earth's crust is thickest
      under high mountains.

8. Which is not true about the paleomagnetic studies related to the plate
   tectonic theory?

   a. they are based on the assumption that the Earth's geographic and
      magnetic poles have never been far apart.
   b. former magnetic pole positions indicate that continental drift,
      of the sort proposed by Wegener, has occurred.
   c. indicate that at various times in the Earth's history the north
      magnetic pole has become a south magnetic pole and vice versa.
   d. they provided the first evidence for actual and measurable
      migration of global tectonic plates.
   e. they led to the construction of a geomagnetic time scale that ex-
      tends well back into Precambrian time.

9. Which is <u>not</u> generally accepted according to present plate tectonic
theoretical models?

   a. Benioff zones, marked by deepening earthquake foci, indicate zones
      where sea-floor plates are descending into the asthenosphere.
   b. earthquakes along transform faults occur only between the offset
      ends of the oceanic ridges, or axes of spreading.
   c. sediments on the sea-floor plates become progressively older with
      increasing distance from spreading axes or ridges.
   d. convection cells in the asthenosphere are the driving mechanism for
      the global plates.
   e. Alfred Wegener's late Paleozoic date as the approximate time for
      the beginning of the fragmentation of Gondwanaland.

10. According to geologists who believe in the phase change theory of
mountain building:

   a. at the "Moho" the change from one kind of rock to another
      occurs entirely in the solid state.
   b. basalt changing to eclogite results in an increase of volume.
   c. the Earth's mantle contains different chemical elements than the
      crust.
   d. uplift of the crust is mainly caused by horizontal compression.
   e. the Earth is entirely molten beneath the crust.

Chapter Nine

DECAY AND COLLAPSE

This chapter deals with weathering and mass gravity movements and is
the beginning of a longer block on the gradational, or "destructive"
geologic processes acting upon the Earth's surface. Chemical and mechanical weathering are treated separately for clarity of presentation, even
though they are usually intimately related in nature. Landslides and related movements are discussed from the basis of Sharpe's basic classification.

In discussing weathering, emphasis should be placed on its general
slowness by ordinary human standards, its great geologic significance
in the breakdown of rock, and its significance as one aspect in the crea-
tion of soil. Here the concept of Uniformitarianism, with its emphasis
on the slow action of everyday processes over long spans of time, can be
profitably emphasized.

Perhaps as important as any idea for the general student is the ever-
present--if often ignored--operation of gravity in the direct leveling
of the Earth's surface. The great variety of mass movements, aside from
the occasional spectacular and devasting landslides, the differences in
rate and type of movement, water content, and different types of material
involved, are points worth making.

<u>Multiple Choice Questions</u>:

1. Weathering is:

    a. largely an adjustment of rocks to high temperatures and pressures
       deep within the Earth.
    b. a purely chemical process.
    c. an active rather than passive process.
    <u>d</u>. responsible for life as we know it.
    e. a form of erosion.

2. Unloading:

    <u>a</u>. involves slight expansion of rock when overburden is removed.
    b. is most effective on sedimentary rocks.
    c. is a form of chemical weathering.
    d. produces mainly vertical joints and rocks.
    e. is a nice theory but lacks supporting evidence.

3. The sedimentary rock most susceptible to chemical weathering is:

    a. conglomerate.
    b. sandstone.
    c. siltstone.
    d. claystone.
    <u>e</u>. limestone.

4. Desilication is most effective on:

    a. limestone.
    b. quartzite.
    c. andesite.
    d. quartz sandstone.
    e. rock salt.

5. Residual waste-mantle results from:

    a. weathering.
    b. erosion.
    c. faulting.
    d. transportation.
    e. deposition.

6. The basic factors of Sharpe's landslide classification are:

    a. streams, glaciers, wind, waves.
    b. soil creep, solifuction, mudflow, slump.
    c. type of movement, rate of movement, type of material, H_2O content.
    d. vegetation, climate, slope, man's activities.
    e. weathering, erosion, transport, deposition.

7. Which mass gravity movement is flowage?

    a. soil creep.
    b. scree.
    c. slump.
    d. subsidence
    e. rock fall.

8. Which is fastest?

    a. lava flow.
    b. landslide.
    c. soil creep.
    d. stream flow.
    e. slump.

9. The Frank, Alberta landslide did not involve:

    a. volcanic activity.
    b. joints.
    c. glaciation.
    d. faulting.
    e. mine collapse.

10. A mass-gravity movement occurring on perfectly flat surfaces is:

    a. slump.
    b. rock fall.
    c. flatulation.
    d. subsidence.
    e. creep.

Chapter Ten

SEAS OF AIR AND WATER

The work of wind and waves is a natural unit that lends itself to discussion of some of the gradational forces acting on the Earth's surface. Wind and waves are intimately related since wind causes the waves that are most significant in modifying the shores. Strictly speaking, the atmospheric circulation that creates winds is in the realm of meteorology. Yet a visual model of the working of winds is worthwhile background for geological discussions. The mechanics of wave action, although overlapping the field of oceanography, are most important to a geologic understanding of shore and coastal development.

It is worth emphasizing that gradation represents the action at boundaries between water, air, and rock as the atmosphere and hydrosphere operate on the Earth's crust, or lithosphere. Wind, although of less direct importance than the other gradational agents, does affect the whole land surface, not just desert regions. Waves today act only on the margins of the lands along the shores of oceans, lakes, and other standing bodies of water, but their far-reaching effects are recorded in abandoned shoreline features and the sedimentary rocks that blanket much of the earth's land areas.

<u>Multiple Choice Questions:</u>

1. Wind-blown sand:

    a. cuts most effectively within one foot of the ground.
    b. may cause the colors in sunsets.
    c. is always composed of quartz grains.
    d. creates dreikanters through the process of deflation.
    <u>e</u>. may create a landform known as a yardang.

2. Sand moves:

    a. as far as 2000 miles in a single storm.
    b. highest in the air over a sand covered ground surface.
    <u>c</u>. mainly by saltation.
    d. as high as several thousand feet above the surface of the ground.
    e. only from higher to lower elevations.

3. Sand dunes:

    a. develop only in arid regions.
    b. cover at least 30% of the Sahara Desert.
    c. do not move themselves although the sand in them does.
    d. are transverse if prevailing wind is strong and sand supply moderate.
    <u>e</u>. always have their steepest side on the downwind or lee side when a slip face is developed.

4. Wind-blown dust:

    a. may form a deposit of loess.
    b. is infertile after deposition.
    c. is rarely deposited in humid areas.
    d. is an important cause of abrasion of rocks.
    e. is always mainly siliceaous in composition.

5. Important experimental studies of sand movement and sand dunes
   were made by:

    a. Robert Sharp.
    b. C.F. Stewart Sharpe.
    c. H.T.U. Smith.
    d. W.M. Davis.
    e. R.A. Bagnold.

6. Waves of oscillation:

    a. are mainly caused by hurricanes and typhoons.
    b. consist of water particles rushing across a water surface in
       sharp crested ridges.
    c. result from submarine faulting, landslides, or volcanic eruptions
    d. have water particles moving in circular orbits.
    e. cause much erosion of the deep ocean bottom.

7. Emergent coastal features:

    a. can be taken as definite evidence of deformation and uplift of the
       Earth's crust.
    b. are represented by drowned shorelines.
    c. always indicate that the present water's edge is on former ocean
       or lake bottoms.
    d. are much more strongly developed on the Atlantic coast of the
       U.S.A. than on the Pacific coast.
    e. are developed only on igneous and metamorphic rocks.
8. Which is a depositional landform?

    a. sea cliff.
    b. stack.
    c. sea cave.
    d. barrier beach.
    e. sea arch.

9. Wave refraction:

    a. is important in modifying gently sloping shores.
    b. causes much more erosion on headlands than bays.
    c. is most common in deep water.
    d. causes wave crests to increase in speed.
    e. tends to make an initially straight shore more irregular.

10. The longshore current:

    <u>a</u>. tends to build sand bars out into open water.
    <u>b</u>. is most active along irregular, deeply embayed coasts.
    c. develops only in salty ocean water.
    d. causes water to move at right angles to a shoreline.
    e. creates sea cliffs in resistant rock.

Chapter Eleven

THE HYDROLOGIC CYCLE

The unifying theme of this chapter, which concludes the discussion of the geological gradational agents, is a mechanical model known as the hydrologic cycle. Since it deals with directly observable phenomena on the Earth's surface, it is a much better established model than those discussed in later chapters that attempt to explain the internal forces of the Earth responsible for mountain building and crustal deformation. The hydrologic cycle involves the work of underground water, surface streams, and glaciers.

Both the economic significance of ground water and its relation to stream flow are important. Streams are the most important geologic agent of land sculpture, and even in the driest deserts their imprint is on the land. The dynamics of stream action are worthy of mention not only for their relation to landforms, but also for their imprint on certain continental sedimentary rocks of the Earth's more remote past. Glaciers and ice ages are generally of considerable interest. Aside from their mechanics and landforms, the uncertain status of theories of ice ages is worthy of emphasis.

<u>Multiple Choice Questions</u>:

1. Underground water:

    a. might flow more readily through a sandstone than through a shale with greater porosity.
    b. saturates rock in the zone of aeration.
    c. is an inexhaustible resource.
    d. flows at about the same rate as water in surface streams.
    e. does not affect the nature of surface streams.

2. Springs:

    a. occur only in areas containing limestone caves.
    b. may periodically spout hot water and steam.
    c. are artificial holes drilled through the water table.
    d. are called artesian springs if found in granitic rocks.
    e. occur only in regions of high rainfall.

3. The source of energy that starts and keeps the hydrologic cycle going is:

    a. radioactivity.
    b. gravity.
    c. the sun.
    d. water.
    e. mountain building.

4. Radial drainage patterns:

   a. indicate that rocks are relatively soft and nonresistant to erosion.
   b. develop on volcanos.
   c. indicate a mature stage of the erosion cycle.
   d. form in rocks that are homogeneous to erosion or in near-horizontal, alternately hard and soft layers.
   e. are the commonest type.

5. The drainage pattern in a region of horizontal strata of alternate resistance to erosion is:

   a. dendritic.
   b. rectangular.
   c. radial.
   d. insequent.
   e. trellis.

6. Streams on claystone transport mainly by:

   a. traction.
   b. saltation.
   c. solution.
   d. gouging.
   e. suspension.

7. Streams in alluvium erode mainly by:

   a. hydrolysis.
   b. corrosion.
   c. hydraulic action.
   d. traction.
   e. corrasion.

8. An erosional landform is a(n):

   a. alluvial fan.
   b. delta.
   c. pediment.
   d. flood plain.
   e. mud flow.

9. The easiest terrain for construction of a major highway would be in which stage of the regional erosion cycle?

   a. youth.
   b. adolescence.
   c. maturity.
   d. old age.
   e. rejuvenation.

10. A youthful landmass in the regional erosion cycle is:

    a. almost at base level.
    b. largely high flat.
    c. near the end of the cycle.
    d. "rough" topography.
    e. glaciated.

11. If an adjusted stream receives an excess on load after a forest
    fire in headwaters, the stream tends to:

    a. dry up.
    b. cut its channel deeper into bedrock.
    c. develop a steeper channel gradient.
    d. back-fill its channel, but keep the same gradient.
    e. develop a more gentle channel gradient.

12. A continental glacier:

    a. now exists in Alaska and also in Greenland.
    b. now covers the North Pole and arctic region.
    c. covered Colorado 12,000 years ago.
    d. covered North America as far south as the Ohio and Missouri rivers
       in Pleistocene time.
    e. produces more rugged and spectacular erosional topography than
       valley glaciers.

13. Glacial ice:

    a. is derived mainly from snow.
    b. forms if rainfall exceeds evaporation each year.
    c. covered half the land areas of the Earth in the Pleistocene.
    d. carves V-shaped valleys.
    e. forms by the freezing of large water bodies.

14. Which landform consists of unconsolidated materials?

    a. cirque.
    b. mesa.
    c. moraine.
    d. hogback.
    e. pediment.

15. The best place for well-sorted deposits of gravel would be in a:

    a. cirque.
    b. outwash plain.
    c. moraine
    d. hogback.
    e. mudflow.

Chapter Twelve

FIXED CONTINENTS TO DRIFTING PLATES

Past presentations of elementary geology had a distinctly pro-
vincial flavor because students tended to be most interested in their
own country and their local surroundings. After the plate tectonic
revolution in the late 1960s, however, textbooks acquired a broader out-
look that included the geology of the world's ocean bottoms. Now, more
and more, students may visit northern Europe, the Alps, the Mediterranean,
and even the Himalayas in this age of easy travel. So it now seems proper
to discuss some of the world's major mountain ranges, which are the vis-
ible products of tectonic mechanisms and thus complete the global picture.

The historical approach to the subject should strengthen the real-
ization that working scientists are not coldly objective and completely
unbiased in their investigations. Clearly geologists do not constantly
go back "to rediscover the wheel". They would make no progress if they
did not rely on the vast store of reliable information accumulated by
their fellow workers and predecessors. Thus they operate within their
contemporary frames of reference--the paradigms and methods learned in
professional education. This normal method of scientific investigation
(as discussed in chapter two) may lead to the exciting episodes called
scientific revolutions. Thus the changing ideas of the origin of mountains, and of continents and ocean basins, tell more about the dynamic
nature of work in science than any cut-and-dried presentation treating
only the latest theories.

<u>Multiple Choice Questions</u>:

1. The theory of the permanency of fixed continents and ocean basins:

    a. never was supported by any geologic evidence.
    b. was first proposed by Dr. James Hutton in the late 1700s.
    <u>c</u>. was the paradigm (frame of reference) for many excellent geologists
       who made valuable contributions to geologic knowledge.
    d. could not account for the presence of marine rocks on the continental
       masses.
    e. gave excellent proof that the Pacific Ocean basin formed when a great
       mass of Earth material was thrown off into space.

2. Concerning theories before 1960 for the source of sedimentary rocks
   in the geosynclines on the North American continents:

    a. they were mainly attempts to fit the field evidence to the theory
       of continental drift.

    b. Dana's theory of Archaen Protaxes was a form of catastrophism.
    c. Schuchert's concept of sunken borderlands was confirmed by geo-
       physical evidence in the 1950s.
    <u>d</u>. Kay's theory that some eugeosynclinal rocks were formed in the
       vicinity of former island arcs survived the plate-tectonic revolution.

36

e. they all accounted for the presence of Benioff zones under the
   Atlantic continental shelf.

3. Gondwanaland was:

   a. first discovered by Captain Cooke.
   b. first proposed by Alfred Wegner.
   c. in the northern hemisphere.
   d. a group of separate continents joined by narrow land bridges.
   e. probably broken up in late Paleozoic time.

4. Which is a correct interpretation of the evidence for Gondwanaland
   that was assembled by Wegener and his followers:

   a. Mesosurus was a medium sized dinosaur.
   b. the Glossopteris flora represents plants of a tropical rainforest.
   c. the general sequence of Gonwana rocks had thick limestones towards
      their base and thick graywackes, melanges, and ophiolite suites
      towards their top.
   d. late Paleozoic glacial deposits are today found in the Antarctic
      and tropical regions of Australia and Africa.
   e. late Paleozoic reptiles are quite different on the different pres-
      ent-day continents but are very similar for Mesozoic and Cenozoic
      times.

5. During the Paleozoic history of Europe:

   a. events were quite unlike those in North America.
   b. the Caledonide and Hercynian orogenies occurred at about the same
      times as the Taconian-Acadian and Allegheny orogenies in North
      America.
   c. the New Red Sandstone was deposited in a tropical coal swamp
      environment.
   d. shelly and graptolitic facies were the dominent rock types during
      Devonian and later times.
   e. the Baltic-Russian Precambrian shield was buried by thick eugeo-
      synclinal deposits.

6. Which is not a present-day theory:

   a. the supercontinent of Laurasia was created by the joining of four
      northern continents at the end of the Paleozoic.
   b. Europe and North America formed a supercontinent until near the
      end of Precambrian time.
   c. the Appalachian and Caledonide mountains of North America and
      Europe were once a continuous mountain chain.
   d. the Ural mountains are a great lava plateau, capped by Pleistocene
      strato-volcanos, which separate the Asian and European landmasses.
   e. rocks in the highlands of Scotland were once part of the North
      American continent.

7. In plate-tectonic theory, the Teth's geosyncline:

   a. formed a great east-west seaway between the northern and southern continents throughout much of Paleozoic and Mesozoic times.

    b. was scoured out by catastrophic ocean currents about six thousand
years ago.
    c. contained limestones and redbeds, but no graywackes or other
eugeosynclinal deposits.
    d. was finally destroyed at the end of Paleozoic time when the Himalaya
Mountains were created.
    e. is a unique geologic feature whose history cannot be explained by
plate tectonic theory.

8. The Alps:

    a. have cores of uplifted crystalline basement that are called massifs.
    b. were explained by Argand and Lugeon as resulting from deformation
along the margins of fixed and permanent continental plates.
    c. are structurally a tremendous tilted fault block like the existing
Sierra Nevada range of California.
    d. contain a great clastic wedge consisting of flysch deposits that
are mainly limestones and glacial deposits.
    e. were completely overriden by the great continental glaciers of the
Pleistocene that overwhelmed most of Europe.

9. Of the many working-hypotheses, hypotheses, and theories that geologists
have proposed for the evolution of the North American Cordillera, which
is now most generally accepted?

    a. the Sevier mountain structures originated when rock masses slid
off a great uplift created by the Nevadan orogeny.
    b. the melanges and granites of the Mesozoic Nevadan orogenic belt
developed above a descending sea-floor plate.
    c. when the east-trending Snake River plains and north-trending Rio
Grande depression intersect each other, the southwest part of the
United States will drift off to form a new subcontinent.
    d. the Basin and Range province results from spreading in the East
Pacific rise where it has slid under the North American plate.
    e. Since the Antler orogeny occurred at about the same time as the
Allegheny orogeny in the eastern United States, the two events are
mechanically related.

10. Among the following interpretations of the San Andreas fault, which is
most certainly not correct?

    a. it formed along the east side of the Sierra Nevada range when the
North American tectonic plate plunged beneath and uplifted crystalline rocks of the Mesozoic-Nevadan orogenic belt.
    b. it is a transform fault between offset parts of the oceanic ridge
represented by the East Pacific rise.
    c. its displacements are caused by the northward drift of the Pacific
sea-floor plate.
    d. it originated when an offset segment of the East Pacific rise was
subducted under the edge of the North American plate.
    e. the Coast Ranges on the west side of the fault are attached to the
oceanic plate and the rocks to the east are part of the continental
plate.

Chapter Thirteen

GEOLOGY, ENVIRONMENT AND THE
ENERGY CRISIS

The importance of geology to human affairs should be obvious. Yet
only in the last decade or so has this "self evident" fact begun to receive proper consideration. Perhaps as an overreaction, many new
courses have been introduced that teach elementary geology, from start to
finish, as applied environmental studies. But without a solid foundation
in the fundamentals of the science, discussions of environmental geology
may lead to oversimplified conclusions. The extremist views of the ardent
environmentalist or the cavalier profit-maker provide no answers to the
growing environmental and industrial problems that have no easy solutions.
Mankind's insatiable demand for nonrenewable resources must be properly
balanced with environmental considerations, all of which are complicated
by the growing human population and the possibility of adverse climatic
changes. We treat these topics in the final chapter to show the relevance
of the geologic record to some of mankind's most critical future problems.

Multiple Choice Questions:

1. The "population explosion":

    a. is not a serious consideration because science will solve all our
       problems.
    b. caused worldwide starvation and millions of deaths in the first
       half of the nineteenth century, just as the Reverand Malthus had
       predicted.
    c. caused a doubling of the world population between 1850 and 1975.
    d. could lead, at the present rate, to a world population of eight
       billion by the year 2010.
    e. is still rapidly continuing in the advanced industrial countries,
       but has stopped in the underdeveloped countries.

2. In relation to agriculture and food production, which is not correct:

    a. there was an excess of farm products in North America in the 1930s.
    b. the "green revolution" in the late 1960s markedly increased the
       world's grain supplies.
    c. the introduction of modern, mechanized farming techniques into the
       less-developed countries requires large expenditures for fertilizers
       and petroleum products.
    d. all tropical soils will form laterite pavements after being plowed
       up for agriculture.
    e. salinization of irrigated lands is possible cause for the downfall
       of the ancient Babylonian civilization.

3. The Holocene ("post-glacial") climate:

    a. began with a general warming trend called the climatic optimum in
       Europe and the altithermal in western North America.

b. has been a 25,000 year period of continuous, benevolent, normal climatic conditions.

c. became known in great detail soon after the European pollen record provided an accurate and detailed method for finite age determinations.

d. is considered to have ended about ten thousand years ago based on age determinations using oxygen isotopes.

e. completely melted away the Greenland continental glacier but not the Antarctic continental glacier.

4. The Little Ice Age (Neoglaciation):

a. was first discovered by the great American geologist, G.K. Gilbert, from field work he was doing in Alaska.

b. caused the rebirth of continental glaciers that spread over most of northern Canada, but never reached the upper Mississippi Valley.

<u>c</u>. was first suggested by Francois Matthes from studies of the Sierra Nevada and the discovery of a salt layer in Owens Lake at the foot of the mountains.

d. began about three hundred years ago when valley glaciers in the high mountains of North America and Europe started their advances that reached as much as 32 kilometers in some places.

e. created great blizzards that burst water mains, stalled auto traffic, exhausted supplies of heating fuels, and caused cold that destroyed much of Florida's orange crop.

5. Which of the following events in human history has <u>not</u> been attributed to climatic change by some scientist studying the problem?

a. the decline and fall of the Indus (Harapan) Civilization.

<u>b</u>. the end of the Minoan Civilization.

c. the abandoned Norse colonies in Greenland.

d. the fall of the black empires in the Sahalian (Sudan) zone of Africa.

e. the destruction of villages in high valleys in the Alps in the 1600s.

6. Concerning the possible crisis in world climates, which statement is most certain in the present state of scientific knowledge?

<u>a</u>. expansion of the great circumpolar atmospheric vortices would shift middle and low latitude belts towards the equator.

b. long term predictions of climatic changes are now possible because of data from orbiting weather satellites and other technological advances.

c. any predictions of major climatic changes in the near future are pure nonsense, according to Professor Reid Bryson.

d. the progressive increase of carbon dioxide in the atmosphere since the start of the Industrial Revolution will cause climatic warming and resulting rises in worldwide sea level.

e. the ever increasing amount of industrial pollution is creating smog that reflects solar energy back into space and will bring on a new major ice age.

7. Coal:

   a. presents few environmental problems in its use and extraction.
   b. is classed as anthracite if the ratio of carbon to other substances
      in it is low.
   c. originated in well oxygenated swamp waters where bacterial action
      was high.
   d. has few good deposits left because mineable world reserves are
      largely exhausted.
   e. has become increasingly important compared to other fuels used in
      our economy.

8. The origin of commercially profitable accumulations of petroleum requires:

   a. an unconformable relation of subsurface rocks.
   b. igneous intrusions into organic shale beds.
   c. a source bed containing abundant remains of trees and other woody
      plants.
   d. underground caverns in which oil pools can gather.
   e. a trap, such as an anticline or fault.

9. Which is correct about the fossil fuels and other natural resources?

   a. fresh water is constantly renewed by the hydrological cycle and,
      therefore, requires no further studies by geologists.
   b. since the Earth's reserves of petroleum and natural gas are ade-
      quate for another 100 years of consumption at the present rate,
      the present energy crisis results entirely from policies of greedy
      oil companies and Arab oil producers who want to make exorbitant
      profits.
   c. in the 1970s the United States, with some six percent of the world's
      population, consumed about one-third of the world's energy production.
   d. deposits of ores for metallic minerals are badly depleted because
      once mined they are gone forever, but the fossil fuels are virtually
      inexhaustible because they are constantly renewed by organic pro-
      cesses.
   e. the world's greatest reserves of coal are in the southern hemisphere
      continents that were once part of Gondwanaland.

10. We can confidently predict that in the twenty-first century:

   a. the population, environmental, and energy problems will have been
      solved by intelligent human planning and international cooperation
      based on advanced technology and science.
   b. solar energy, geothermal heat, and wind power will meet all energy
      demands that now depend upon oil and gas.
   c. breeder reactors that produce no dangerous waste materials will be
      in operation.
   d. nuclear fusion will meet all industrial requirements and allow the
      generation of hydrogen to replace diminished gasoline supplies.
   e. it is not certain that any of the three preceding statements are
      correct.

Textbooks

A number of excellent textbooks are listed in the Suggested Readings
at the end of each chapter.

Dictionaries and Glossaries

<u>Dictionary of Geologic Terms</u>, prepared under direction of American
Geological Institute, Dolphin Books of Doubleday & Co., Garden
City, New York, (1962): contains some 7500 terms from geology
or related sciences. It is a simplified and abridged version
of the A.G.I. Glossary, quite adequate for most student and teacher
needs.

<u>Glossary of Geology and Related Sciences</u>, edited by American Geolog-
ical Institute and published by the A.G.I., Washington, D.C.,
(2nd edition, 1960): contains about 17,000 geologic and related
terms, good item for your library.

Junior High School Earth Science Materials

<u>Investigating the Earth</u>, sponsored by American Geological Institute,
published by Houghton-Mifflin Co., Boston, (1967): stresses in-
vestigative approach to earth science, accompanied by extensive
teacher's guide, and a laboratory manual.

<u>Geology and Earth Sciences Sourcebook for Elementary and Secondary</u>
<u>School Science Courses</u>; Holt, Rinehart, and Winston, 383 Madison
Ave., New York,(1962): this guidebook is designed to give science
teachers ready access to essential information for instructing
students in geology and related sciences.

<u>Project Ideas in the Earth Sciences</u>: U.S. Geological Survey,
Washington, D.C.: free on request. Describes various science
club project possibilities in the geological sciences.

Career Opportunities

<u>Geology, Science and Profession</u>, American Geological Institute,
1444 N St., NW., Washington, D.C.: describes the requirements for,
and work in the geologic profession. For high school students.

<u>Opportunities in Geology & Geological Engineering</u>, Vocational Guid-
ance Manuals, 212 485th Ave., Bayside, New York.

News

<u>Geotimes</u>, published by American Geological Institute, 1444 N St. NW.,
Washington, D.C.: a good way to keep up to date on news in geologic areas, also contains interesting columns, articles, and ad-
vertisements.

Laboratory Manuals

A large number of laboratory manuals are available from many sources.
Two companies producing many manuals are:

Wm. C. Brown Co., Inc., Dubuque, Iowa.

Burgess Publishing Company, 426 South Sixth St., Minneapolis, Minn.

Separate exercises may be purchased through:

Laboratory Studies in Geology, by J. C. Brice, J. R. Miller and
    Robert Scholten, (1962): 23 separate pamphlets, W. H. Freeman &
    Co., 600 Market St., San Francisco, Calif. This series covers
    a wide range of geologic subjects to be treated in laboratory ex-
    ercises. Affords the opportunity to introduce new and varied
    approaches to elementary laboratories in geology.

Films

Directory of Geoscience Films, American Geological Institute, 1444 N
    St., NW., Washington, D.C.: this is the best general source for
    information on films. It is an annotated listing of more than 500
    films on geology and related sciences. Usefulness of each film
    for educational purposes and an indication of suitability for var-
    ious groups from junior high school through college are given.

Maps: Write for information to:

Map Distribution Section, U.S. Geological Survey, 1200 South Eads St.,
    Arlington, Va. 22202: for geologic or topographic maps east of
    the Mississippi River.

Map Distribution Section, U.S. Geological Survey, Federal Center,
    Denver, Colorado 80225: for maps west of the Mississippi River.

Erwin Raisz, 107 Washington Ave., Cambridge, Mass.: for physiographic
    and landform maps.

Geographic Press, C. S. Hammond Co., 517 Valley St., Maplewood, New
    Jersey: for physiographic and landform maps.

Williams & Heintze Map Co., 8119 Central Ave., Washington, D.C.,
    20027: for student collections of geologic maps.

Air Photos

University of Illinois Air Photo Repository, Univ. of Illinois,
    Urbana, Illinois: for catalogue (1967) of student study sets of
    stereo-pairs of geologic and other phenomena.

U.S. Geological Survey, (either of the addresses given previously for
    maps) for index maps of photo coverage and general information for
    obtaining photos. Best have areas of particular interest in mind.

ISBN: 0-442-25314-1